D0559889

SOUND SENSE

SOUND SENSE

THE INSTRUMENTS OF THE ORCHESTRA
AND HOW THEY WORK

GEOFFRY RUSSELL-SMITH

TABOR COLLEGE LIBRARY
Hillsboro, Kansas 67063

BOOSEY & HAWKES

760349

BOOSEY & HAWKES
MUSIC PUBLISHERS LIMITED
295 REGENT STREET LONDON W1

and at

Paris · Bonn · Johannesburg · Sydney

Toronto · New York

© 1965 by Boosey & Hawkes Music Publishers Ltd.

All rights reserved

PRINTED IN ENGLAND
BY H. FITCH & CO. LTD.

CONTENTS

*I am indebted to my various friends in the Instruments Division of Boosey &
Hawkes who provided so many photographs of instruments together with invalu-
able technical advice, and also the following for their kindness in allowing me
to reproduce photographs and other materials: The B.B.C.: photographs of
Paul Tortelier and Frederick Wigston—page 12 and diagram of the human ear
—page 38; Messrs. Gauthier-Villars: the oscillograms and wave analyses
(reproduced here as histograms) taken from "Accoustique—Analyse des Sons
Musicaux; C.R.S.A. 24 avril 1939" by Mlle. Andres Damman—page 40; The
Curators of the Horniman Museum: photographs of Ecuador pan-pipes—page 5
and Sumerian Harp —page 33; L. W. Hunt Drum Co. Ltd.: photographs of
gong drum—page 29; The Curators of the Science Museum: photographs of
Thomas Alvar Edison and The Phonograph—pages x and xi; Mr. G. A. Briggs,
of The Wharfdale Wireless Works Ltd.: the photograph of a recorder player
and oscilloscope—page 40.*

I
ON JUST MAKING A NOISE

Sound is usually something we can't get away from; the sound of cars and their horns, footsteps, the wind in the trees, people talking or dropping things—incidental noises. Add to this intentional noise; the sound of televisions and radios, the 'ping-pong' of the ice-cream van, bicycle bells, fire bells, door bells—all competing for our attention, and it's lucky that we can control a sort of mental switch and shut them out, or at least turn them down a bit.

Despite this, most people have only a sketchy idea of what sound really is.

"It's—sort of—vibrations, isn't it?"

It is in fact many sorts of vibrations, and before really understanding the instruments of the orchestra one must return to the basic business of how sound is made, how it travels, and how we hear it.

Perhaps the first thing to remember is that air is elastic. If you put your finger over the end of a bicycle pump you can squeeze all the air up to one end; and when you let go the handle bounces back just like a spring.

Imagine what happens when you bang two things together, a ruler on a table for instance. Now a table is elastic—more elastic than, say, a block of concrete—and the force of the ruler hitting it moves the table-top; it moves only very slightly, but it does move suddenly and quickly, and the air round the table receives a sudden jolt.

The air then acts rather like a line of coal wagons in a shunting yard when the engine is being coupled. Hit one wagon and it moves, squeezing its sprung buffers against the next wagon which in turn presses its buffers against the next, and so on all down the line. Anyone who has tried to sleep near a shunting yard while this is going on will know that this "wave" takes quite a long time to reach the other end of the train.

The jolt of our table being hit sends a wave of movement through the air (in all directions, not just down a railway line) until, a fraction of a second later, the air jostles our ear drums and we hear the sound. Usually there are several jolts, pushes and pulls as the table bounces back into its former position.

Suppose we now select a number of articles that have an obvious springiness; a wooden ruler (after all it is springy enough

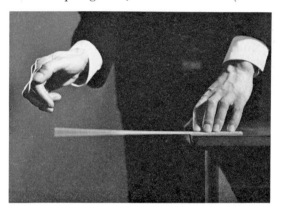

to flick paper pellets), an elastic band and a piece of clock spring. If you rest the ruler over the edge of the desk so that about two-thirds protrudes, holding it down firmly with one hand, you can twang the other end and produce quite a musical note—a note you could sing, unlike the noise of banging the desk. You can do the same with the piece of clock spring. The elastic band, stretched between only your fingers can twang quite a musical sort of sound.

All you need then to make sound is something that vibrates. You can't shake your hand fast enough, but a humming bird's wings will produce a loud hum, and bees and flies whose wings beat even faster sound different notes again. The mosquito (and don't forget it's the female that buzzes and she's the one that bites) beats her wings even faster to produce that ominous high-pitched whine.

Things which are elastic or springy and so vibrate with a regular frequency are, with very few exceptions, the basis of all musical instruments, and some further very simple experiments can be used to demonstrate more of the basic principles of music making.

If you hammer an ordinary dress-maker's pin a little way into

a piece of wood, so that about three-quarters of it is showing, you can twang it with another pin to make quite a pleasing clear note. I remember that, when I was a boy, I carefully hammered a whole row of pins into a length of wood taken from the side of an old box; making use of the fact that the less pin there was showing the higher was the note, I made a simple instrument on which I could play recognisable tunes.

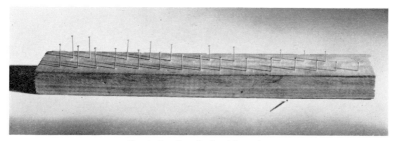

Facsimile of my boyhood invention.

One point worth mentioning here is that this musical toy of mine (dubbed the "pini-piano") didn't rely on the tiny movement of the pin itself to disturb the air around it and thus produce the sound, for the pin alone would have made a sound almost too quiet to hear. However, as the pins were mounted on a light piece of wood, the vibration of each pin shook the wood at a similar speed, and so most of the sound one really heard came from the piece of wood which made a simple *sound board*.

Incidentally, if you examine the works of a musical box you will find a metal comb with teeth of differing lengths. When the

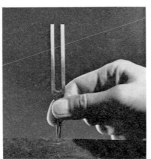

mechanism's tiny barrel revolves, the pins on it twang these teeth as they go past, producing sound in exactly the same way.

If you have watched a piano tuner at work, you will have noticed how his tuning fork makes a very tiny sound when he bangs it on his knee, but as soon as he presses the base of it on the piano lid, it suddenly makes a louder sound. He is in fact doing what I did with my "pini-piano"— making the strong vibrations of a small object set up similar ones in a larger one in order to "shake" more air and produce a louder sound.

So far we have been thinking of air purely as something used to carry sound from the instrument to our ear. But, if you remember, air is elastic, and so we can play tunes on it. Of course, one can't pick up a piece of air, just like that! One can, however, put it in something, a bottle for example, and then start making sounds with it. Naturally an empty bottle already has air in it and all that is needed to make a musical note is to make the air bounce.

POP

PIP

It is just the same as twanging our elastic band or plucking the notes on the "pini-piano". Pull a cork out of an empty bottle and the "pop" that you hear is made by the air inside being slightly "stretched" as the cork comes out, and then suddenly bouncing back. Do this with a tall thin wine bottle and you will produce a fairly low note; use a small aspirin bottle and the sound will be much higher in pitch.

There are of course other ways of making such a *column of air* vibrate in a container. Blow across the open end of your pen-cap and even first time you will probably produce a good strong whistling sound. This is because your mouth sends a stream of air straight against the far edge of the tube. Some air goes down inside it, and some escapes. The air that goes into the tube slightly compresses the air already in it, whereupon it bounces out and gives an extra puff to the spare wind spilling over the edge. Immediately some more air goes down the tube, compresses its contents, and the whole process is repeated. All this happens so quickly that the stream of air spilling over the side is mixed with hundreds or even thousands of extra tiny puffs every second which come from the air bouncing in the tube.

If you look at a simple tin whistle, the sort that comes out of a Christmas cracker, you will see that when you blow it, the air goes down the mouthpiece, sometimes called the *wind-way*, so that it emerges pointing at a straight edge, known as the lip or *fipple.* This arrangement produces the same effect as blowing across the pen-cap. The lip or fipple splits the stream or air; some goes inside the tube, gets compressed, bounces out and joins the main stream spilling over the side.

As one would expect, a whistle with a long tube makes a lower note than one with a short tube, and a series of different length whistles side by side will make quite a respectable instrument. You can buy one made out of plastic for about two shillings from your local music dealer or toy shop. These are still sold under the original name of *Pan-pipes.* I remember my own set cost twopence, and the celluloid it was made from tasted delicious.

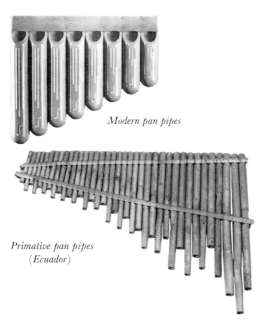

Modern pan pipes

Primative pan pipes (Ecuador)

This instrument has a very long history indeed, for examples of Pan-pipes have been discovered dating back many thousands of years. The more primitive sets lacked the windway and fipple of the modern variety, and the player had to blow across the open tops of the tubes on the "pen-cap whistle" principle.

This idea of a set of different length tubes, each one producing a different note, was a bit inconvenient if you wanted all the notes over a wide range; and an important step forward was made when it was discovered that a tube open at both ends would produce a similar sound, although somewhat higher in pitch and a little quieter in volume. In the tube open at both ends, the air stream splits at the fipple as before, and again some goes down the tube and some spills over the edge. Now, although the bottom of the tube is open, the air outside it offers a certain amount of resistance to the free escape of wind, and so some still bounces back. An open ended tube however is much easier to shorten—you don't need to keep cutting pieces off the end. All that is required is a series of holes cut in the side of the tube covered with your fingers; when you raise your fingers from the holes, the tube acts as though it were

5

shorter, the part below the open holes having very little effect. In this way it is possible to produce many different notes from the same tube.

Section through the recorder

Those of you who play the recorder will know that this isn't quite the whole story, and that sometimes the part below the open hole can make a difference to the pitch of the note, but these are details to be explained later. Certainly if you take a recorder (or even a tin whistle), cover all the holes, and then open them up one at a time starting at the end furthest away from the mouthpiece, you will play some sort of scale.

RECORDERS AND FLUTES

The recorder then is a simple tube with a wind-way and fipple at one end, open at the other, and having a series of holes in its barrel which the player covers with his fingers. Although you can buy a very good modern plastic one for about 14/0, in their heyday (before 1750), they were made of wood or bone and were very respectable, serious instruments used for both ensemble and solo work. Henry VIII had a number of "chests" of recorders. A "chest" consisted of one each of the five sizes of instrument, from the biggest, the *bass* recorder, to the smallest, the *sopranino*. The sopranino incidentally was so high and shrill that it was often omitted from the recorder ensembles, and the standard *consort* was made up of the lower four instruments only—*descant, treble, tenor* and *bass*.

Recorders were also played together with stringed instruments in the very small mixed ensembles of the day.

The one great drawback to the recorder however is that the low notes are very quiet indeed, while the upper ones are always loud. If you try to make the low ones louder by blowing harder, the instrument *overblows*, that is, it suddenly jumps up an octave (eight notes), and if you blow harder still, it will sound another note even higher. This difficulty over controlling the loudness of the instrument could obviously be a serious one when playing with other instrumentalists, and was largely the cause of its decline in popularity.

The *transverse flute*, the recorder's greatest rival, had been in existence for some hundreds of years, and although the player had to use the "pen-cap whistle" method of blowing, it had distinct advantages.

It had been found by experiment that, instead of blowing across the open end of a tube as in the pan-pipes, you could block the end off completely and put a hole in the side quite near it. Blowing across this hole would then produce a similar sound, but with the tube turned round sideways. Strangely enough it was found that the quality of the notes improved while the fingering was no less comfortable than that of the recorder. Most important of all, the player could control the volume or loudness of his instrument.

To play quietly he merely made the space between his lips smaller (and blew more gently) so that the stream of air from the mouth was narrower, and struck less of the edge of the hole. The recorder on the other hand had a fixed wind-way which carried an air-stream which was always the same width, and so couldn't be varied.

Here is a simple flute (about 1700). It has one key. This has a round pad mounted on one end which closes the end hole on the

An early 18th century one-key flute

instrument so that the player need not stretch his hand to cover this hole with his little finger. Compare this with the modern flute and its little brother the piccolo:

A modern flute

A modern piccolo

N.B. These photographs are not to scale as the piccolo is only about half the length of the flute, but the enlarged view shows how complicated both these instruments have become.

III
VIOLINS AND OTHERS

Let us go back to our elastic band to arrive at some basic notions of how a stringed instrument works. Of course a piece of rubber has much more stretch in it than the steel or gut string of a violin, but we can use this extra elasticity to do some simple experiments without having to use the sort of tension found in real instruments.

If you merely put the elastic band round a book for example, the best sound you can make is a sort of "thwack" as you lift it up and let it slap down against the surface of the book. But slip a pencil under one end, and you have something that looks vaguely like a musical instrument. Now if you have your *bridge* near one end, you can pluck the rubber band to make a fairly good note. You can also shorten the vibrating part of the rubber by putting a finger down on it near the other end. This of course is what a violinist does when he wants to produce different notes, and a few moments' practice on your elastic-band violin should produce some quite recognisable melodies.

Anyone who has had anything at all to do with violins (or other members of the orchestral string family) will know that, unlike guitars, for example, they are mostly played with a bow. If you

look at a violin you will see that it is shaped so that the bow can cross from the top string to the bottom one without touching wooden body of the instrument. Before discussing the violin itself however, the bow is worth examining in some detail.

The "business" side of the bow is made of horse-tail hairs which have been mounted on a springy wooden stick.

They lie in a sort of flattened bunch, about half an inch wide, and are stretched between the tip-mounting and the *heel*—the part you hold. If you look at the two pictures at the bottom you will see that the stick naturally curves towards the line of the hairs. However, there is a *tail-nut*

The violin

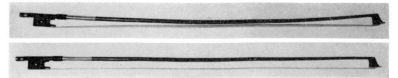

The bow

9

which, when screwed up, pulls the heel along the stick and so tightens the hairs, thus making the stick almost straight.

The strings of the instrument themselves are made from steel or gut (sheep-gut, not cat-gut), and are sometimes covered with a layer of wire wound tightly round the string itself to give it extra weight. Now in order to make the hairs of the bow grip the strings and make them sound, the player rubs a little block of resin (musicians pronounce this *"rozin"*) on the hairs, so that some rubs off as a slightly sticky powder. You can take a well-resined bow and produce notes from violin strings, wine glasses, wood-saws,

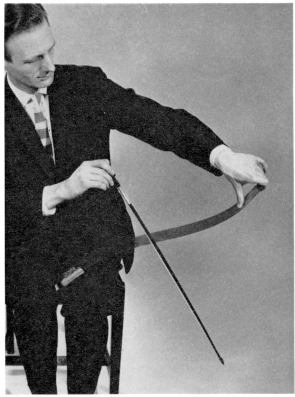

hand bells—in fact anything that has a nicely defined edge that will vibrate. (Don't try playing on the teeth side of the saw; use the back and bend the blade across your knee to put the metal under stress.)

The way in which a bow makes a string vibrate is really very simple. The hairs are pressed lightly against the string, and pulled steadily across it. The resin helps to

How to play the saw

make them grip the string and so pull it slightly out of line. The string however, being under tension overcomes the pull of the bow. It promptly springs back, but in fact over-shoots its original straight-line position, whereupon its further return is helped by the movement of the bow. After two or three tiny false starts, the string vibrates at its natural frequency, and will go on sounding for as long as the bow keeps moving. Even a change in the direction

10

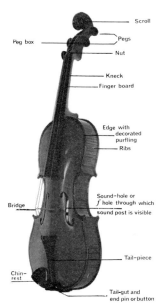

Scroll

Peg box

Pegs

Nut

Kneck

Finger board

Edge with decorated purfling

Ribs

Bridge

Sound-hole or f hole through which sound post is visible

Tail-piece

Chin-rest

Tail-gut and end pin or button

The various parts of a violin

of the bowing, if well handled, will produce only the tiniest interruption in the flow of sound.

Of course the shape and construction of the violin is very important. If you remember, a thin string vibrating won't disturb very much air and so can only make a tiny sound. But the violin is built to produce the maximum resonance with the string's vibrations being transmitted via the bridge to the two large surfaces at the front and back of the instrument. You will see from the photograph that the violin is hollow, and the *sound-post*, visible through the f hole, not only helps to support the pressure of the bridge, it also carries these vibrations through to the back of the instrument.

There are two of these decorative f holes cut in the front of the instrument or *belly*, and these allow the vibrating body of air inside to increase even further the volume of sound already produced by the exterior surfaces.

In brief then, the player uses his bow to make the strings vibrate between the nut and the bridge. The *pegs* in the *peg-box* are used to tighten the four strings when tuning. At the top of the peg-box one usually finds the carved *scroll*. The other end of the strings, below the bridge, are attached to the *tail-piece*. This in turn is attached to the bottom of the instrument, the *end-pin* or *button*, by means of a *tail-gut*, a thick loop of special gut string for the purpose. The *finger-board* lies roughly parallel to the strings, and just below them so that the player can press them down onto it. This of course shortens the vibrating length of the string and thus raises the pitch of the note.

In the modern orchestra there are four sizes of instrument belonging to the string family, the Violin, the Viola, a larger violin, and played in the same way, the Violoncello, usually called the Cello, which is held between the knees with its weight supported by a *tail-pin*, and the Double-bass, which is so large that the player must stand up or use a tall stool.

Incidentally, the viola has a range that lies very awkwardly across the treble and bass staves, and one of the less usual C clefs is used. This is a sort of curly bracket, and the middle of this sign

The great Paul Tortelier playing the cello at a B.B.C. concert.

The double bass being played by Frederick Wigston, member of the Royal Opera House orchestra, Covent Garden.

points at the third line of the stave indicating that this line is being used as middle C. The open strings of a viola are thus more usually written:

The members of this family can all be played in a number of different ways. The players can use their bows (Italian: *arco*), pluck the strings (Italian: *pizzicato*, pronounced "pits-i-cart-o") or even, very rarely, bang the backs of their bows on the strings to make a chippy noise (Italian: *col legno*, pronounced "coll lenyo", meaning literally, "with the wood").

One thing the string family can demonstrate superbly is an effect that is the subject of our next chapter—*harmonics*.

IV
TWICE ONE IS TWO

I have used this as a chapter heading in order to establish in the reader's mind that the basic arithmetic of a vibrating string is very simple indeed. It is however essential in the understanding of the chapters which follow.

A very pretty series of experiments can be done with a stringed instrument or a simple one-string fiddle which can easily be constructed from a piece of scrap wood. If you are going to use a real instrument for demonstration, a cello is better than a violin, because its strings vibrate widely enough for you to see clearly what is happening.

Let's assume you have neither violin nor cello and therefore need to make our experimental one-string fiddle.

Take a narrow piece of wood about two feet long. Drive an ordinary screw into one end and a screw cup-hook into the other. Make two simple supports, one for the bridge proper, and the other, the smaller of the two, for the nut. Now tie a length of cello string to the screw at one end, pass it over the primitive bridge and nut, and attach the other end to the cup-hook so that when you screw the hook down you tighten the string. You now have something that looks like this:

All the following experiments can be performed by plucking the strings—*pizzicato*. However a bow will maintain the vibrations for as long as you want, so borrow a bow if you can, and don't forget to tighten up the hairs before you begin, and rub on a little resin. (It is even more important to slacken the hairs again when you have finished; otherwise its owner may never lend you anything again.)

First pluck or gently draw the bow across the string. You will see that it vibrates quite strongly along its whole length and looks like this:

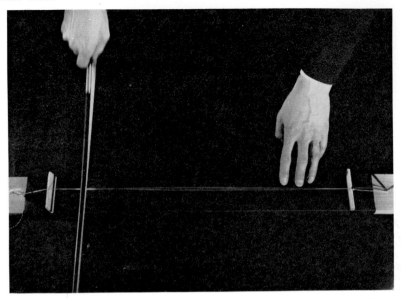

Now press down the string an inch or so from the nut and you will sound a higher note.

Now here's the trick! While bowing the string, lightly touch it in the middle. Don't press it, just tickle it. The effect is immediate and you may find it surprising.

The string at once starts vibrating in two equal sections producing a new note. It looks like this:

Perhaps most important of all, the new note you are sounding is an octave above the previous note produced. If you were to take a slow motion film, you would be able to see it move from

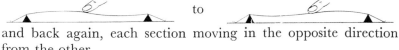

to

and back again, each section moving in the opposite direction from the other.

Now these half-strings vibrate at twice the speed of the full-length string. It's rather like a two-foot pendulum which swings at twice the speed of a four-foot one. If the open string vibrates at 200 times a second, and you put a finger lightly on the middle, the two halves will vibrate at 400 times a second. If the open string sounds 🎼 (about 128 vibrations per second), lightly touch it in the middle and the string will sound 🎼 (about 256 vibrations per second). Your finger makes a dead point where the string doesn't vibrate at all. We call such a point a *node*.*

Now suppose you shift your finger along so that it is one-third of the way along the string, you produce a new note and the string vibrates like this with a second node forming all by itself.

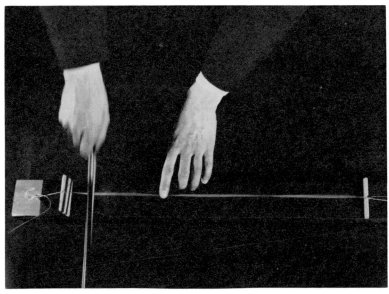

* The place where the string vibrates most, about half-way between two nodes is called the *antinode*. As we are concerned here with the formation of nodes however, the term *antinode* is not used again in this book.

You can demonstrate that the spontaneous node is not vibrating by resting a paper pellet across it while the string is in motion. Anywhere else along the string the pellet will fly off, but at the node it will—with a little persuasion—stay in place.

The three sections, each vibrating three times as fast as the whole string, gives the note  at 484 vibrations a second. The same thing happens if you touch the string a quarter of the way along its length; it will vibrate in four sections each vibrating at 512 per second.

These notes are called *harmonics*, and the open string sounds a note called the *fundamental*. The harmonics then form a series of notes above the fundamental which vibrate two, three, four, five, six, seven, etc., times as fast.

This series when written down looks like this:

128   128x2 128x3 128x4 128x5 128x6 128x7 128x8

You will see from all this that each time you go up an octave you double the number of vibrations per second. Go up a fifth (that is *doh* to *soh*) and you multiply by $\frac{3}{2}$; to go up a fourth (*soh* to *doh'*), multiply by $\frac{4}{3}$; a major third (*doh* to *mi*) by $\frac{5}{4}$, and a minor third (*mi* to *soh*) by $\frac{6}{5}$. The next fractions produce some rather odd intervals so we shall not go any further.

It should now be clear that, in terms of frequencies (vibrations per second) the difference between the pitch of two notes is usually a simple fraction.**

A string player may sometimes be required to produce such harmonics as a special effect in a piece of music. The sound is very thin and steely in quality, and of course such notes cannot be played *vibrato* (a term used to indicate the slight shaking of the player's left hand that provides the warm singing quality of modern string playing).

Harmonics and the harmonic series however play a prominent part in the way brass instruments work and so it seems sensible to examine these next.

* The sixth harmonic, shown here as B♭, is a note that lies outside the natural scale, and sounds distinctly out of tune.

** You will see from the diagram however, that when the two notes concerned are more than an octave apart, the calculation may require two or more fractions multiplied together.

16

V
SOUNDING BRASS

Whilst we may think of the strings as being the romantics of the orchestra, the brass—Horns, Trumpets, Trombones and Tuba have a rich, dramatic quality. Their job includes the playing of brilliant fanfares, rich-sounding chords and many other musical effects which add colour and warmth to orchestral music.

Despite this, they are essentially simple in construction and working, although the precision of manufacture, and the amount of hand-work needed to produce them, makes them fairly expensive to buy.

Basically, a brass instrument consists of a long tube with a cupped *mouthpiece* at one end, and a flared *bell* at the other, like this:

As you already know, any tube contains what musicians and scientists call a column of air, and as with the flute or recorder, the player's task is to make this column vibrate. In a brass instrument however he does this by an entirely different method. If you stretch your lips into a sort of humourless grin and blow, you can produce a distinctly vulgar and non-musical sound. Do this however with your lips pressed against the cup of a brass instrument's mouthpiece and the vibrations set up by your mouth will induce the column of air in the instrument to vibrate; the pitch of these vibrations will of course be governed by the length of the tube.

Playing the "plastic post-horn"

If you can borrow a trumpet or trombone mouthpiece (preferably the latter), try putting it into the end of about six feet of garden hose pipe. You will then have a very limited but quite playable instrument—a sort of plastic post-horn. A shorter piece of tubing will do almost as well, but you will need to tighten your lips much more to produce any note at all, and about six feet is a convenient length to experiment with.

17

A few minutes spent in blowing noises on your plastic instrument will demonstrate that, although the length of the tube remains the same, you can produce a number of different notes. As one might guess, however, they are all notes from the harmonic series, and since your six-foot instrument is roughly in the key of F, it will play approximately these notes:

Imagine what happens when your lips are tight enough to produce a middle C. This sets up vibrations which are the natural "bounce" frequency of a two-foot tube and so our six-foot tube becomes divided by nodes of non-vibrating air into three separately vibrating sections each two feet long. When you sound the next F up, the column of air divides into four sections and so on, like this:

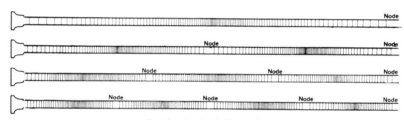

Simple tube divided by nodes

You will see that there is a node right at the end of the tube where the vibrations meet the resistance of the still air outside the tube. This is called the *terminal node*, and because the air is travelling down the tube, and also because the vibrations at this point are spreading out in all directions, this terminal node actually lies just outside the instrument.

To return to blowing our plastic post-horn. If we do manage to blow the bottom note or fundamental (and it's a very difficult note to get), you will hear that it has a rough quality quite different from the other notes. Brass players only very occasionally sound this note, and so different is its quality that it has the special name of *pedal note* as though it were played with the feet (a term borrowed from the organist's vocabulary).

So we now have a length of tubing capable of sounding *doh—soh—doh'—mi'—soh'—(ta'?)—doh"*. All that is needed to provide an instrument which can sound other notes is some sort of device to alter the length of the tube and enable the player to produce a complete new harmonic series. The simplest of these is the *slide* on the trombone with one tube fitting inside the other. It works like this:

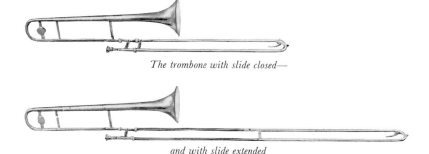

The trombone with slide closed—

and with slide extended

You can see from the photographs above that when the player pushes the slide out, the tube becomes longer. He can in this way lower any of the notes in the harmonic series by up to six semitones. If he starts on a *soh* with the slide closed, six semitones lower will produce a *ra*, one semitone above *doh*. He then has only to close up the slide in order to play the *doh*.

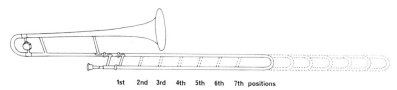

1st 2nd 3rd 4th 5th 6th 7th positions

He can of course keep blowing while moving his slide from one position to another and so produce the 'Music Hall' effect of slithering from one note to the next. This effect is known as *glissando* or *portamento*. For serious playing, however, he uses the slide in seven positions—the closed position and six extensions, and stops blowing while moving from one note to the next.

Important though it is, the trombone is only one of the four brass instruments usually found in the orchestra. The others use valves instead of slides. A brass instrument's valves have one function in life—to introduce a short piece of extra piping into the instrument in order to lengthen it. The middle valve on a trumpet, for example, works as shown on the next page.

19

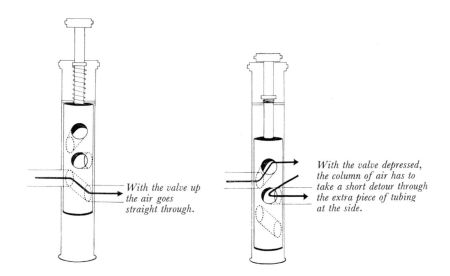

With the valve up
the air goes
straight through.

With the valve depressed,
the column of air has to
take a short detour through
the extra piece of tubing
at the side.

Like the trombone in closed position, these instruments with no valves depressed sound a natural harmonic series. Depressing the valves does the same job as extending the slide on a trombone; they lower the fundamental and its series of harmonics by up to six semitones. One doesn't need six valves for this because a player can push down more than one valve at a time, and by using different lengths of detour-tubing for each valve, only three valves are needed. You will see these on the trumpet below.

The first valve (the one on the left) lowers the fundamental by a tone, the second by a semitone and the third by a tone and a half.

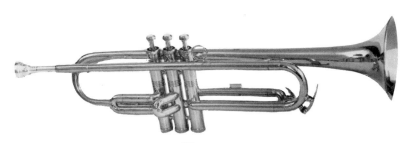

The trumpet

This arrangement is also used for the (French) Horn and the Tuba (the lowest sounding of the group) although these days you will see instruments, particularly horns, which employ *rotary* valves instead of the older *piston* type. There is however no difference in the effect of this newer design except to make an easier and faster action.

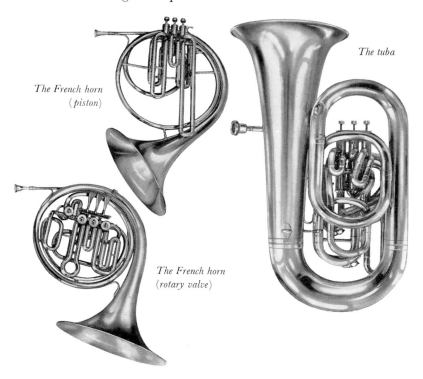

The tuba

The French horn (piston)

The French horn (rotary valve)

Now the horn itself has a very wide compass of notes from up to about . This is due to the fact that it has a very narrow bore compared with its length. The narrower the bore the easier it is to produce the upper harmonics. It is also easier to play those not intended and produce wrong notes. Because of this and other factors, a horn may sometimes be fitted with a fourth valve operated by the player's thumb. This by-passes a length of tubing and thus *transposes* the whole instrument up a fourth (from *doh* up to *fah*). An instrument with this addition is known as a "Double Horn".

Before going into the differences in range and tone of the various members of the brass family (which are dealt with later on) it would be useful to return to the woodwind.

21

VI
REEDS—SINGLE AND DOUBLE

The only member of the woodwind family so far mentioned has been the flute and its predecessor the recorder. This instrument, you will remember, uses the simplest way to make its column of air vibrate and we should now consider the Clarinet and Oboe which, by contrast, use *reeds*.

The reeds of clarinets and oboes are slices of cane cut and shaped so that, when placed in the player's mouth, his breath will make them vibrate in a way very similar to a brass player's lips. This sets up vibrations in the column of air in the instrument.

Some woodwind instruments employ *single reeds* and some *double*, and it is essential to remember which is which. Thus the clarinet takes a single reed. An oboe on the other hand takes a double reed: *An oboe reed* a thin flattened tube made from two pieces of cane.

In the first case the single reed vibrates against the solid *lay* of the mouthpiece, and in the second the two thin edges of the double reed vibrate against each other.

A clarinet reed

You will remember from our examination of brass instruments that the range of notes we can get from a column of air is vastly increased as soon as we employ harmonics. The oboe, for instance, has *two special *octave-keys* which produce these harmonics by inducing nodes, and open these small holes in the tube and thus produce the first and third harmonics. One would normally expect to find these about half-way down the instrument for the first octave and a quarter of the way down for the second octave. In fact the tiny octave-key holes are quite near the reed for reasons which I shall explain.

Look for a moment at the recorder again. Play up the scale from the lowest note (C on a descant). The first octave is simple, but when you start on the second octave you have to crook the left thumb and push the thumb-nail into the small hole in the back of the instrument. Now this successfully divides the column of air into two equal parts, but every further note up the scale has the effect of shortening the lower part of this division; so the thumb-nail stops being half-way down the column. Because of this the player has to persuade the column of air to form a node a little higher up by

* With some instruments only one is employed.

22

closing other holes at the bottom. If you look back to page 15 you will see that the second harmonic on a string is produced by producing a spontaneous node. The recorder player can do the same thing by using fingering like this:

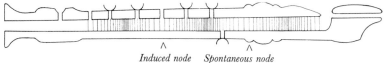

Induced node   Spontaneous node

The end section vibrates at its natural frequency, thus causing the upper section to vibrate in two halves divided by a node.

Now the oboe, because of this shortening of the tube when the player goes up the scale, has its very tiny octave-key holes much higher up than the half-way point. When these keys are opened they provide a sufficient interruption in the flow of air to set up a *turbulence* in the vibrating column and so induce a node at the correct place.

Of course the player need not use either of these to blow a harmonic. If he merely *overblows*, and puts too much pressure of wind into the instrument it will sound the note an octave higher exactly like a brass instrument. The sound it makes, however, is very coarse, and some of the over-blown notes are out of tune. The octave-keys are therefore required (together with cross-fingering) to play in the middle and top registers.

Today an oboe, like other woodwind instruments, is covered with a profusion of levers and pads called *keywork*, all of which combine to make the player's task easier. You will appreciate that for rapid passage-work, with runs and trills and so on, a simple tube with holes along its length is too clumsy, and too many of its notes will be out of tune if approached in an untidy and hurried manner. The keywork removes at least some of the anxieties of playing the simpler instruments.

The oboe

Another point to remember is that the player has two delicate pieces of cane between his lips, and is controlling both lip-pressure and breath-pressure. At the same time, he is also gently touching the tip of the reed with his tongue at the beginning of each phrase or group of notes. It is obvious then that a well-balanced, easily fingered instrument is very necessary if he is to control the delicate sounds which the oboe can produce.

The oboe, like the violin, has a number of big brothers, sounding deeper notes, although working on the same principle.

23

The Cor Anglais is a sort of alto oboe. Despite its name, which is sometimes translated as "English Horn"; it is neither English, nor is it a horn. It has however an angle or bend in it, and the probable origin of its name is the French *Cor anglé* or Angled Horn. One more feature which makes it easily distinguishable is the onion-shaped resonating chamber at the lower end.

The next member of the family, a sort of bass oboe, is the Bassoon. The tube of this instrument is about eight feet long, and obviously it would be very inconvenient for a player to have a great length of tubing like that sticking out in front of him so the bassoon has been "folded up".

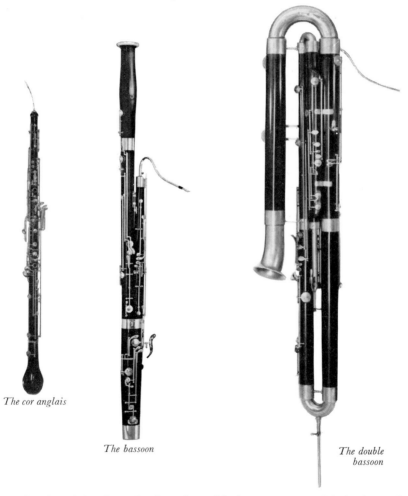

The cor anglais

The bassoon

The double bassoon

The bend in the tube has the added advantage of bringing all the holes reasonably near each other.

The largest member of the family, the Double Bassoon (*see opposite page*), is rather an orchestral luxury, and is used mainly in pieces written for very large orchestras. It sounds an octave lower than the ordinary bassoon, and so has twice the length of tubing. It is worth noting that, as a brass instrument needs only three valves to add to its overall length, the instrument can be coiled up into a very small space—a sort of plumber's nightmare. A woodwind instrument, however, needs holes punched along most of its length, and these must be accessible to the fingers or at least to padded keys, and so the design of the larger woodwind instruments is a very complicated business.

The only single reed instrument which needs describing here in detail is the Clarinet. So far the cross-sections of instruments hasn't concerned us very much. The trumpet, for example, is made from tubing roughly the same width all the way through, whilst its cousin in the Brass Band, the Cornet becomes steadily wider throughout its length. They are however both played in exactly the same way, the only difference being one of tone, and the cornet is described as having a *conical bore*. The oboe likewise has a very tiny tube leading from the double reed, becoming wider all the way down to the open

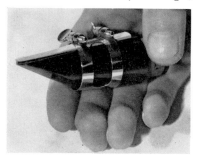

A clarinet mouthpiece

bell end. The flute, on the other hand, is obviously equally wide all the way. This we call *cylindrical bore*.

Now the clarinet has a single reed, a simple slip of cane, cut flat on one side and with one end shaved to a curved edge. This is held by a *ligature* to the lay of the mouthpiece. The whole fits on to the end of an instrument which is cylindrical except for a slight flaring at the bell end.

The clarinet

For rather obscure reasons, due to its cylindrical bore, when this instrument is overblown by the player it produces, not the octave harmonic, but the next one. We say that it "overblows the twelfth"—the interval concerned being a twelfth or twelve notes above the fundamental. This means the clarinettist must employ additional holes to reach the first possible harmonic (i.e., the twelfth), and so the instrument's compass is roughly divided into three sections which sound quite different. The lowest notes, deep and oily in sound, form the *chalumeau* register (pronounced "shall-oo-mow"); the *break* is a rather dull register of notes between the top of the bottom octave and the *twelfth;* the top register is bright and clear. The three sections of the compass cover the following notes:

Chalu-   Break   Top
meau   register

Like so many instruments, the clarinet has a big brother, the

The bass clarinet

26

Bass Clarinet. This plays an octave lower, and thus has to be made from twice the length of tubing. As you can see, due to this extra length it has to be curled at both ends, and looks somewhat like a Saxophone. The saxophone, however, has a very different sound due to its conical bore; a sound, in fact, which will not blend at all well with the other orchestral woodwind and brass. It is for this reason rather than any question of musical snobbishness which has caused it to be generally omitted from the symphony orchestra. It has, nevertheless, made occasional appearances as a soloist in concertos and rhapsodies.

The saxophone

VII

DRUMS AND PERCUSSION

This book started with the simple notion of producing sound by hitting a surface—a desk with a ruler—but the complete percussion section of the orchestra cannot be dismissed so lightly. Certainly some of its members are very complex and deserve detailed description.

Probably the most useful and frequently used instruments in this section are the kettle-drums or Timpani. Each drum or "timp" (there are usually two or three; sometimes more), consists of a skin mounted on a thin hoop frame, and called the *head*, and stretched over a large copper *kettle* or *shell*. Until recently the head was made from the dressed skin of a sheep or other animal. Nowadays however it is often made from a thin sheet of special plastic.

The player tunes his drums to sound specific notes. The trouble is that every *A timpano (plural : timpani)* time he changes a note he has to tighten up or slacken the skin by the tuning screws or "taps". This of course takes time, and each re-tuning needs checking before the player makes his next entry. The timpanist's job has thus become one of producing rhythms (not forgetting the sustained thundery roll) on notes which occur within the orchestra's harmonies. Until a few years ago, the only melodies he could produce were ones made up from the two or three notes his drums were tuned to. The recently invented Pedal Timpani can however change their pitch very quickly, so that the player can play a simple melodic passage on one drum, and even produce a change of pitch while the drum is actually sounding. This *glissando* (a sort of "*boing!*") was of course quite unknown until the last few years.

The invention is, of course, quite splendid from the player's point of view, but unfortunately each pedal timp costs about six to eight times

The pedal timpano

as much as the classical type adjusted by hand. Composers in the past never dreamed of the luxury of instant tuning for this instrument, and so it is only in a few modern works that this new invention is really necessary.

Unlike timpani, the Bass Drum has two heads mounted on opposite sides of a large hoop. Naturally when one is struck the opposite one resonates with it.

The bass drum

The sound produced is very low in pitch, and it is very difficult to say exactly what note is being produced. In consequence it is used as though it had no particular pitch, and composers feel free to combine it with any chord without fear of its clashing with the harmonies played by the rest of the orchestra.

Sometimes a single-sided bass drum (or Gong Drum) may be employed. This has a head on one side only, and is much larger in diameter than the double headed variety.

One of the most familiar sounds from the percussion section (sometimes called the "kitchen department") is the dry, rattling

The gong drum

chat of the Side Drum. This is quite a small affair less then two feet in diameter.

The picture shows one resting on its stand. What the picture does not show is the snare on the underside. This consists of three or four pieces of gut string (about the thickness of a cello D string), or sometimes coiled wire which lie across the surface of the lower head so that when the drum is played, they rattle against the skin to produce the instrument's dry "chippy" noise. By pressing a lever on the side of the drum, the player can disengage the snare.

Composers sometimes call for a Military Drum which is like the ordinary side drum, but you will see that it is somewhat different in proportion. It has snares, but is much deeper in pitch.*

The side drum

Cymbals, made from a brass alloy, hardly need description. They can be used in pairs and clashed together, or a single one suspended from the middle can be struck with a felt-headed or wooden stick. A roll with a soft-headed stick produces that ominous sound beloved by film and television play producers.

The Triangle with its delicate but penetrating "ting", and the "clackety-clack" of the Castanets are so familiar that they deserve only passing reference here.

The military drum

A cymbal

The triangle

Castanets

* There is also a Tenor Drum, which looks like the military drum, but doesn't have any snares.

30

There is however a group of instruments in the percussion family which stands apart from the noise-makers or excitement-builders. These are the *tuned percussion*, consisting of all those instruments which posess a complete range of notes and are played with hammers or beaters.

Perhaps the one with the longest history is the Xylophone (pronounced Zy-lo-fone—*Xylos* is the Greek for wood).

This consists of a series of long, thin blocks of hard wood of differing length, which are laid out on a frame. A modern xylophone has these blocks arranged like the piano keyboard.

You will also see from the photograph that under the blocks there are tubes suspended; These are the resonators.

A modern orchestral xylophone

So far in this book we have dealt with the resonance of the soundboard, the violin's surfaces, the hollow belly of stringed instruments, drum heads and so on; these are all *variable pitch* resonators. Now, in the xylophone, the tube under each note is open at the top and supplies a column of air which will vibrate at the same frequency as the block of wood above it. When the note is struck it sets up resonance in the tube (these, in *fixed pitch* resonators, are sometimes called *sympathetic vibrations*) and thus increase the volume of sound.

Looking rather similar, but producing a totally different sound, is the Vibraphone. This has metal plates instead of wood blocks, and each plate gives a clear, bell-like tone. Again each note lies above a tubular resonator, but at the top of each of these tubes in the vibraphone there is a disc mounted on a long rod which runs the length of the instrument. The rotation of this rod, driven by clockwork or an electric motor at one end, makes the resonators open and shut as each disc is presented edgewise or flat at the open end of the resonator.

The result is a clear, singing tone with a sort of *vibrato*. The sound is somewhat sentimental, and it is more often used in light orchestral music than in serious symphonic works.

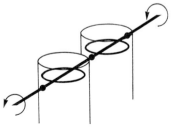

How the vibraphone works

Somewhat similar, but lacking the *vibrato* of this instrument, is the Glockenspiel (from the German *Glocken:* bells; *spielen:* to play). This is a much smaller affair, normally covering only three

31

octaves. It usually lacks any resonators, and its sound is thin and icy-clear.

The glockenspiel which is played with beaters should not be confused with the Celesta which also has metal plates. These are mounted inside a cabinet (looking rather like a harmonium) and the player performs on a keyboard. As he is not limited by having to use a pair of beaters, one in each hand, the celesta player can play much more complicated music suitable for the piano-like action of his instrument, where the depression of each key causes a felt-tipped hammer to strike the metal plate immediately above it. If you want to remember what this instrument sounds like, simply recall the ice-like sparkle of the *Dance of the Sugar Plum Fairy* from Tschaikowsky's *Nutcracker Suite*.

One instrument, the Orchestral Chimes achieved enormous popularity in the 19th century, when much of the music "told a story".

A set of chimes consists of a series of long steel or brass tubes hung on a frame and struck with a leather covered hammer which is shaped rather like a chairman's gavel. The sound each note makes is very similar to a distant church bell, and is identical with the modern "Westminster Chime" door-bell.

There are a number of other percussion instruments required for particular compositions, but as this book is intended to cover the standard orchestra, we shall not include them here.

Orchestral chimes

VIII
THE HARP

*Sumerian harp from Ur
about 2000 B.C.*

Modern pedal harp

The Harp has an extremely long history, and was originally used to accompany the solo singer. If you remember, David in the Old Testament sang while accompanying himself on the harp.

The modern orchestral harp is vastly more complex and very much louder than the earlier harps. The principle has however remained unchanged and you will see from the illustrations that its forty-seven strings are stretched between the tuning pins at the top, and the large sound-board at the side.

Now, although the instrument is capable of playing nearly every likely combination of "black" and "white" notes, if you slowly run your fingers across the strings of the instrument you will hear the '*doh-re-mi-fah-soh-la-te-doh*' of the ordinary scale.

All of this is achieved by a very cunning arrangement of pedals which stick out from the foot of the instrument. These pedals are connected by a series of levers to seven rods which pass up the inside of the pillar. A further set of levers operates a series of discs along the top of the instrument. Each disc has two projecting pins so that as it turns they 'stop' or shorten the string.

Each pedal has three positions, but let us assume to begin with that all the pedals are in the second position, or half-way up. Like this you can play straight up the scale of C major. But if you push down the F pedal to the bottom position, all the Fs on the instrument become shortened through the movement of a series of pins attached to small wheels up near the tuning-pegs. This shortening makes every F into an F♯, and so we are now in the key of G.

If, instead of pushing down the F pedal, you raise all the B pedals to the top of the stroke, all the Bs become B♭s, and you are in the key of F.

By having one pedal for each white note of the scale, you can play in any key, and move from one key to another by changing the pedal positions whilst playing.

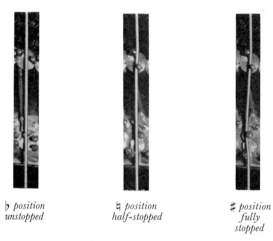

♭ *position*
unstopped

♮ *position*
half-stopped

♯ *position*
*fully
stopped*

One special effect on the harp is the *glissando*—that splash of sound made by the player's hand sweeping across the strings. Now the "black" notes all have two names; in other words E♭ may be called D♯, and B♭ can also be thought of as A♯. Suppose you wanted to play this chord 🎵. All that is needed to make the G♯ is to press down the G pedal.

If on the other hand you wanted to make this sort of sound on the same chord:

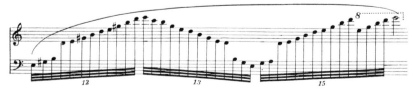

34

you would need to prepare the pedals so that your hand, passing up or down the strings, would not sound any unwanted notes. It would then be necessary to set the pedals like this: E, F♭, G♯, A♭, B, C♭, D. Each string would then sound a note from the chord, and the fact that three of the notes are sounded twice in each octave would not be noticeable because your hand travels so quickly. This delightful effect can be pure magic, providing the composer has the good sense to reserve it for real highlights in the music.

Another wonderful sound obtainable from the harp is the simple harmonic which the player produces by touching the string lightly with the thumb or edge of the hand (at the half-way point to produce a node) while plucking the string. A harp harmonic is a very quiet, distant sound, but beautifully clear in tone.

IX

NOTES ON THE PIANO

The Piano or Pianoforte (Italian *piano:* soft; *forte:* loud) is not normally used as an orchestral instrument, but it is a good idea for all music students to have some notion of how it works, and at least a sketchy knowledge of its ancestors.

I think most people are aware that a grand piano consists of an iron frame, shaped somewhat like a harp laid on its side, and having a *keyboard* which operates a series of hammers which in turn strike the strings when the keys are depressed.

As you would suspect, the longer and heavier the string the louder the tone and deeper the pitch, although one can use long strings for the higher notes, but they have to be under greater tension. In a modern "grand" the strings are so arranged so that the bass strings actually cross over the higher ones (without actually touching them) and the space inside the instrument is used more economically. (This is known as *overstringing*.) Furthermore, in order to produce a fairly even volume of tone over all the range, the middle notes all consist of two strings per note, and the upper ones, three. When a hammer in the middle range strikes a note, it actually hits two strings at a time, similarly with the three strings in the upper register. The lower strings are much thicker than the ones at the top of the piano, and are made of a steel core with a covering of brass or copper wire spun onto them, while the ones for the upper end of the instrument are single strands of steel. The iron frame on which they are stretched is attached to a thin sound-board made of varnished pine. The complete set of strings exerts a pull of just over thirty tons!

When a note is played, a felt covered hammer is thrown against the string and then falls back sufficiently far to allow the string to vibrate. As long as the key is held down, the hammer is locked in position by a *check action*, which prevents its bouncing up and down and striking the string again. If you have ever heard a piano where the check action has "gone" you will realise why this is necessary, as without this mechanism each note sounds like a short burst on an electric bell.

At the same time, as the hammer strikes the string a felt-covered *damper* (one for each note) is raised to allow the string to vibrate, and when the key is released the damper falls back into place and so cuts off the sound. The exception to this is when the pianist wants the note to go on sounding and presses the *sustaining pedal* (the right-hand one)—usually called quite wrongly "the loud pedal".

His left foot operates the *soft pedal* which, on a grand piano has the startling effect of moving the whole action, keyboard and all, about a third of an inch to the right. This brings the middle range hammers opposite one string instead of two, and the top ones opposite two strings instead of three. In this way all except the bass of the instrument is working, so to speak, at reduced power.

The piano has a number of predecessors including the *Clavichord* and the *Harpsichord*. In the clavichord, instead of hammers bouncing off the strings, a metal *tangent* strikes the string near one end and remains pressed against it so the longer section vibrates. The shorter section is permanently damped with a strip of felt threaded in and out of the strings. Its tone is very quiet indeed, so quiet that it is said that the boy Handel managed to practice the instrument in secret in the attic of his home without fear of being overheard.

The harpsichord on the other hand produces a robust "twangy" sound as tiny *quills* or leather *plectra* (Latin *plectrum:* a quill) actually pluck the strings. When the quill plectra are used the instrument sounds rather like a Spanish Guitar played by a performer who has forgotten to cut his finger nails.

The harpsichord is also a very much larger and more complicated instrument and often employs up to five separate sets of strings and two *manuals* or keyboards. It also has a number of *stops* like an organ which are used to bring into play several sets of strings at once, or change over from quill to leather plectra. Some instruments even go so far as to enclose the strings in a *swell box* which has movable shutters like a Venetian blind so that the player may increase or decrease the volume while playing.

Although to some extent the harpsichord is considered a museum piece, it can be heard today as there has recently been a revival in its playing and manufacture.

TABOR COLLEGE LIBRARY
HILLSBORO, KANSAS 67063

X

WHY DOESN'T A TRUMPET SOUND LIKE A VIOLIN?

Common sense tells us that there is no reason why it should! On the other hand, if both instruments are playing middle C, for example, they are both producing 256 vibrations per second.

Before going on, we have to go back to our original notions of what sound is and how we hear it.

In each ear we have a tiny ear drum (called, not sur-prisingly, a *tympanum*), and when there is any increase in air pressure, our ear drums bulge inward very slightly; if there

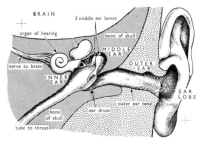

The human ear

is a drop in pressure, they bulge out. Anyone who has been up in an aeroplane will know that as the aircraft climbs his ears start "popping". This is because the air pressure becomes less the higher one is above the ground, and the ear drum starts to bulge slightly outwards. The action of swallowing opens the *eustachean tubes* to the throat and so equalises the pressure again between the air outside and that in the ear itself.

Now if we induce a series of very tiny changes in the air pressure around us, the ear drum will register these changes by slightly moving in and out; if such changes occur fast enough, we will "hear a sound".

I remember a book I once read in which sound waves were described as being like waves on a pond. The wave-producer, a floating block of wood, was waggled up and down, and the waves spread out from it so that a celluloid duck on the other side of the pond bobbed up and down in a similar pattern. Three waggles on the floating woodblock produced three bobs from the celluloid duck a few moments later. Not only this, but "echoes" could be bounced off the side of the pond as shown. On the same pond one could see waves passing through each other, either as echoes or waves from two different sources vi-brating at different speeds.

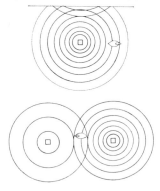

The celluloid duck, quite naturally, bobbed up and down in time to the waves that passed under it, and even a mixture of two sets of waves from different sources was recorded in the duck's movements.

Now air isn't a flat surface, and sound-waves do not consist of tiny hills and dales like the waves on a pond, but we can still use the hill-and-dale idea to describe the push-pull effect of air on our ear drums, and the high and low pressure waves which cause it.

One very old experiment (which incidentally partly inspired Edison to invent the Phonograph) can be done very easily by anyone who owns or can borrow a tuning-fork. First tie a short piece of horse-hair to one of the prongs of the tuning-fork so that it protrudes about half an inch. Then smoke a small piece of glass over a candle. (Keep the glass moving or it will crack with the heat.)

If you now sound the tuning-fork by banging it on your knee, and then draw it across the glass so that only the horse-hair touches it, you will produce a *graph* of the sound wave—a picture of the sound.

Enlarged view of part of the line drawn by a tuning fork.

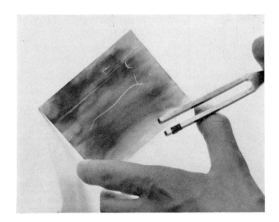

Of course you cannot use smoked glass and horse-hair for tracing more complicated sound waves, and so we have to use a *cathode-ray oscilloscope.*

This is like a television receiver which traces a scan-line from side to side on the tube. When a microphone is connected up with the circuit, the pushes and pulls which move the diaphragm of the microphone are traced on the screen as up and down waves.

A note from the tuning-fork is a simple *sine wave* as shown on the smoked glass on the previous page.

The *wave forms* from other instruments however are more complex. Some of these are shown on the right.

These complex patterns are due to the fact that nearly every instrument produces a number of different sounds at the same time. When you play middle C, you make a sound which is not only middle C, but included in the sound is the next C above, the G above that, then C, E, G, (B♭,) C and so on. The fact is almost every note consists of a fundamental and a complete series of harmonics all sounding at the same time. These quiet harmonics are called *upper partials*.

The recorder being played into a cathode-ray oscilloscope

Wave forms of:

TROMBONE

CLARINET

VIOLIN

Now, whilst the frequency of the fundamental gives the pitch of the note, it is the relative amount of each upper partial that provides the characteristic sound of the instrument.

Here are some diagrams of the relative strength of upper partials for these three different instruments.

Relative energy output of fundamental and upper partials from wave forms shown above

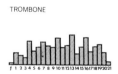

TROMBONE

ƒ 1 2 3 4 5 6 7 8 9 10 11 12 13 14 15 16 17 18 19 20 21

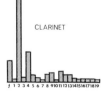

CLARINET

ƒ 1 2 3 4 5 6 7 8 9 10 11 12 13 14 15 16 17 18 19

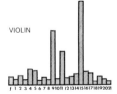

VIOLIN

ƒ 1 2 3 4 5 6 7 8 9 10 11 12 13 14 15 16 17 18 19 20 21

Once you grasp the idea that upper partials are present in all sound, you will understand how we can talk and make ourselves understood, why "oo" doesn't sound like "ee", and why a violin doesn't sound like a trumpet. You will also appreciate how by registering these upper partials, our ears can distinguish between one instrument and another.

The sounds which come from an orchestra all arrive as pushes and pulls in the air, and our ear drums vibrate in and out with these changes in pressure. It is the brain translating this into music which is the real mystery of sound, and such things lie outside this or any other book so far written.

APPENDIX I

THE COMPASS OF INSTRUMENTS AND TRANSPOSITION

A note on transposition

A number of woodwind and brass instruments *transpose*, that is, they are not built in the key of C. A clarinettist or trumpeter who has a B♭ instrument, for example, will read [music notation] but the sound from his instrument will be [music notation]. Because of this, music for B♭ clarinets and trumpets has to be written one tone higher than that for other instruments of the orchestra. When the orchestra plays in C, these instruments must play in D. A little puzzling-out will show that such instruments are built in two flats, so every time they play, their music must have either two *less* flats or two *more* sharps. When the orchestra's key signature is: [music notation] theirs must be [music notation] and when it is [music notation] they must play in [music notation]. This brings them into a key one tone higher, and every note in their parts must of course be written one note up as well.

Some instruments transpose up or down an octave. This merely means that they play in the same key as other performers, but their instruments sound an octave higher or lower than written.

THE WOODWIND

The (Concert) Flute (see page 7)

A woodwind instrument* with its sound produced by blowing across the *fipple-hole* or *embouchure-hole* at one end. It has a cylindrical bore and a compass of [music notation]. The sound is clear and shrill in the upper register and warm and quiet in the lower. It does not transpose.

---

* These days flutes are often made of metal—nickel-silver, silver or even gold—but are still considered members of the woodwind family owing to their method of producing the sound.

i

The Piccolo (see page 8)

This is a miniature flute with a compass of  which sounds an octave higher than written. It produces a shrill brilliant sound and is used mainly for decorative and rapid passage-work.

The Alto Flute (see page 8)

This is usually, and quite incorrectly called the *Bass* Flute. It sounds a fourth lower than the concert flute. It transposes and has a compass of [music] written [music].

(*The Bass Flute* proper sounds an octave below the concert flute, and is written an octave higher than its sound.)

The Oboe (see page 23)

A double-reed woodwind instrument with conical bore. Its compass is [music].

Its sound is somewhat nasal and plaintive excepting in the top register where it can sound very delicate, at the same time penetrating.

The Cor Anglais (see page 24)

A double reed instrument like a large oboe. It has the characteristic angle or bend near the reed, and an onion-shaped resonator at the foot.

Also conical in bore, its compass is [music]

It is however a transposing instrument, and its music is written a fifth higher giving a written range of [music].

The Clarinet (see page 25)

A single reed instrument with a mainly cylindrical bore. The orchestral player usually has two—one built in B♭, and the other in A. This means that he rarely needs to play in difficult or remote keys.

The compass is written [music] sounding one tone lower on the B♭ instrument and one and a half tones on the A.

The Bass Clarinet (see page 26)

This sounds an octave lower than the B♮ mentioned above, and is also transposing. The music for it is written a ninth higher than sounding.

This gives a compass of [musical notation] written [musical notation]

The Bassoon (see page 24)

A double reed instrument with a conical bore. Although its high notes can sound beautifully plaintive, it usually plays in the bass and tenor registers where its tone is rich and fruity. Its compass is

[musical notation] to [musical notation]. It does however use one of the C clefs

which are customary for instruments whose compasses lie right across middle C. The top note of its register, the B♭, appears as

[musical notation] when written in the Tenor Clef.

The Double Bassoon (see page 25)

A double-sized bassoon which has a usual compass of notes

written [musical notation] which sound an octave lower.

Its tone is very thick and rather like a friendly fog-horn.

THE BRASS

The (French) Horn (see page 21)

A brass instrument with a very wide compass—written [musical notation]

The horn is a transposing instrument, usually built in F (there are others) and so it sounds a fifth lower than written. The

actual compass of the F instrument is [musical notation].

Its tonal range is very wide, from the quiet caressing sound to pure fury in loud passages. As the instrument is supported with one hand actually inside the bell, the player can *stop* or hand-mute a note by merely partly opening his hand so that a quiet note is even more distant, and a loud one quite menacing. These aggressive noises are called *cuivre* or *brassed* and are marked in the music

with a small cross, like this [musical notation]. The modern Double

Horn cuts out a length of tubing when an extra valve, played with the thumb, is depressed, bringing the whole instrument into B♭. *

* This principle is also sometimes used for trumpets, trombones and tubas.

The Trumpet (see page 20)

A brass instrument with a clear tone. Its compass is .

It is often a transposing instrument in B♭ sounding one tone lower than written. Trumpets in C, D, E♭ and even F are also in use, but the last three are usually reserved for those works which originally included them written by composers living between about 1650 and 1760.

The (Tenor) Trombone (see page 19)

This is the instrument with a slide mechanism. Although it is built in B♭, it does not transpose, and the player develops his technique of reading accordingly.

Its compass is .

Occasionally it employs seven pedal notes (see page 19) from down to .

The Bass Trombone (see page 19)

Built in G or F (B♭/F) it is non-transposing.

It has a compass of or .

The Tuba (see page 21)

Built in F (or E♭), and again non-transposing, this three-valve instrument is the deepest in pitch of the brass group. It is often used in conjunction with two tenor and one bass trombones to make a low-pitched brass quartet.

Its compass is for the F instrument

or one tone lower for the E♭. Tubas of other sizes are used in Brass and Military Bands, but need not concern us here.

THE PERCUSSION

In the Percussion Section many of the instruments have no fixed pitch, and so the following list is naturally incomplete. (see page 28)

The Timpani (see page 28)

Consisting of two, three or even four drums, the usual compass is [notation] . Very small, high-pitched timpani are sometimes needed sounding up to [notation] .

The Harp (see page 33)

Consists of a frame on which 47 strings are stretched. These are plucked with the fingers. Tunes to the scale of C♭, a series of seven pedals give a full chromatic range of six and a half octaves, [notation] to [notation] It is capable of chords and melodic passages, also *glissandi* on a number of chords.

The Glockenspiel (see page 32)

A chromatic instrument consisting of metal bars which are struck with beaters. It has a written compass of [notation] which sounds two octaves higher than written.

The Xylophone (see page 31)

A chromatic instrument made of wooden blocks mounted over tubular resonators and struck with beaters. Its compass is [notation] sounding as written.

The Vibraphone (see page 31)

Resembling a xylophone in appearance, it employs metal plates mounted over tubular resonators. Each resonator is connected by a rotating rod which carries a series of damping plates which choke the resonance as it revolves.

Its compass is [notation] sound as written.

The Celesta (see page 32)

The metal bars producing the sound are enclosed in a wooden case, and felt-covered hammers are connected to a keyboard by an *action*.

Its compass is [notation] sounding as written.

THE STRINGS

The Violin (see page 9)

A stringed instrument, tuned in fifths [♪] and having a compass of [♪].

It is usually played with a bow, although *pizzicato* and *col legno* passages are written for it (see page 12).

The Viola (see page 11)

A larger version of the violin, it is also tuned in fifths [♪] its compass is [♪].

The Cello (*Violoncello*) (see page 12)

Larger still, played between the knees with its weight supported by a tail-pin, the cello also has four strings tuned in fifths to [♪]. It has a compass of [♪].

The Double Bass (see page 12)

The player has to stand up or use a very tall stool to play this, the largest member of the family. It has four strings, but due to the distance the player has to stretch his fingers to produce the various notes, it is tuned in fourths instead of fifths: [♪].

Its compass is written [♪] sounding an octave lower.

Owing to its gruffness and extremely deep pitch, it is rarely used for solo passages, and normally plays the bass notes of the harmonies, sometimes doubling the cellos, or playing rhythmic figures *pizzicato*. One delightful exception to this is the notorious and amusing double bass solo called *the Elephant* from Saint-Saëns's *Carnival of the Animals*.

APPENDIX II

CONVENIENT FALLACIES

Throughout this book I have used certain ideas which, although quite valid as illustrations, are not entirely accurate. I would not like my younger critics to condemn this little book because certain details did not exactly agree with the facts learned in the elementary physics laboratory! I therefore intend tying up these loose ends.

Pressure and Suction (see page 4)

Those of you who have done even the simplest experiments in air-pressure will know that there is no such thing as suction. When you drink milk through a straw you start off with a equal air-pressure of some twelve pounds per square inch pressing on all surfaces. The pressure of air down the straw is equal to that pressing on the milk all round it. By closing your lips on the straw and making your muscles increase the space inside your mouth, you reduce the pressure inside the straw. You now have twelve pounds per square inch pressing on the surface of the milk round the straw, and slightly less inside it. So the milk is pushed up the straw like water coming out of an ornamental fountain.

Now I mentioned "stretching the air" in connection with the sound made by pulling a cork out of a bottle. The real effect of this is to reduce the pressure of air in the bottle as the cork starts coming out. Once the cork is far enough out to allow passage of air past it, the outside pressure forces air in at considerable speed. Due to the *elasticity* of the air, its *mass* and also its *speed*, a slight over-compression occurs in the bottle and so sets up a bounce for two or three vibrations—enough to establish a note of definite pitch.

Pitch and Vibrations per Second

Up to now I have used a series of "vibrations per second" for sound at various pitches which are a little different from the ones commonly found in present-day musical instruments. The figures I have used, however, are so convenient for calculation purposes that they are always used by physicists when dealing with the mathematics of sound. This series is called *philosophical pitch* and is based on the notion of the octaves of C being produced by 1, 2, 4, 8, 16, 32, 64, 128, 256, 512, etc., vibrations a second. The first four numbers in the series are inaudible, however, and sixteen vibrations per second sound a very low thundery note which occurs only on large pipe-organs.

If an instrument were tuned to this pitch, it would sound roughly a semitone flat of a normally tuned one, giving, for example, 427 vibrations a second for A. The *international standard pitch* is tuned to A=440 vibrations per second. However, as relative pitch is always a matter of exact *proportion* (see page 16), these differences have no effect on our experiments or conclusions.

APPENDIX III

JUST INTONATION AND EQUAL TEMPERAMENT

The intervals found on a modern keyboard instrument are deliberately slightly mis-tuned. If you ask a violinist to play B♭, he will produce a different note from his A♯; an oboist will adjust his *embouchure* or mouth-position to do the same thing. On the piano, however, two such notes are the same. The problem arises like this.

If you go up in octaves from the bottom C on the piano, the vibrations per second double for each octave:

| 32 | 64 | 128 | 256 | 512 | 1,024 | 2,048 | 4,096 |

If however you go up in perfect fifths, the vibrations are normally multiplied by $\frac{3}{2}$:

| 32 | 48 | 72 | 108 | 162 | 242 | 464.5 | 546.75 | 820.125 | 1,230.188 |

| 1,845.281 | 2,767.922 | 4,151.783 |

You will see from the above workings that by going up in fifths, and ignoring the fact that D♯ is not really the same as E♭, you finish with a top note which seems to have both 4,096 and 4,151.783 vibrations a second, depending on which route you took.

Therefore, in order to have a keyboard which is reasonably in tune in all keys the octaves must be accurate, but all other intervals slightly mis-tuned or adjusted (tempered). A piano tuner in fact tunes the middle octave in fourths and fifths, and then slightly flattens or sharpens one of the notes each time so that the interval produces about three *beats* a second. This he does "by ear".

We have all heard pianos that are slightly out of tune and where some notes beat with a wavering quality. This is because one of the two or more strings hit by a hammer vibrates at a slightly different speed from the other and the vibrations of the faster keep on catching up with the next vibration of the slower, like this:

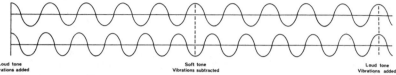

Loud tone
Vibrations added   Soft tone
Vibrations subtracted   Loud tone
Vibrations added

The same effect is produced with notes that are not quite a fifth apart because the upper note vibrates one and a half times as fast as the lower.

It is interesting to note that Bach wrote his Forty Eight Preludes and Fugues (one in each major and minor key) in order to promote the use of *equal temperament* as this deliberate mis-tuning is called.

Keyboard instruments up to that time were tuned to *just intonation:* that is, all the white notes were perfectly in tune with each other, and the black notes sounded C♯, E♭, F♯, G♯ and B♭. Other instruments had split black notes, one half sounding the flat and the other the sharp.

They were all very badly out of tune in remote keys (those with many sharps or flats), and it was largely Bach's genius in the "Forty Eight" that established permanently the principle of *equal temperament*. Anyone who wanted to play this particular work had to use an instrument tuned thus and in fact the "Forty Eight" is sub-titled *Das Wohltemperirte Klavier* (The "Well-tempered Keyboard").

·APPENDIX IV·

THE REPRODUCTION OF SOUND

The two principal pioneers of this field were Alexander Graham Bell and Thomas Alvar Edison, the first as the inventor of the telephone, and the second of the Phonograph.

Now, while Bell's telephone was electrical and Edison's Phonograph mechanical, it is unlikely that Edison's invention would have occurred when it did without the idea of a vibrating diaphragm having been developed through Bell's early work on telephones.

Essentially, when you speak into a telephone your voice sets up vibrations in the plate mounted in the mouthpiece. This plate carries behind it a small container of powdered graphite or carbon. This powder is quite a good conductor of electricity when compressed, but rather a poor one when loosely packed.

Supposing you pass an electric current through the carbon while speaking into the mouthpiece. Every sound wave that presses on the diaphragm will allow a stronger current to pass through the circuit each time the carbon particles are compressed. You will appreciate that the electric current is being *modulated* or altered in strength in a pattern exactly the same as the movement of the plate.

Now include in our circuit an electric magnet which is mounted a fraction of an inch away from a similar soft iron plate. Every increase in current will increase the strength of the magnet and thus distort the plate and pull it toward the magnet, and the sound of your voice is reproduced.

Edison's invention of the Phonograph came about almost by accident. In 1877 he was working on ideas for a repeat-telegraph, having telegraph messages, consisting of dots and dashes, automatically recorded on strips of paper. He also wanted a machine that he could feed additional strips of paper through which had been previously prepared so that messages would be automatically transmitted. One of the purposes of all this was that such machines could be speeded up to work much more quickly than a human operator. It seems, however, that at this sort of speed the machines picked up chatter from the paper tapes which reminded Edison of human speech. This, in conjunction with Bell's new invention, set him thinking, and in the autumn of that year he had his technician John Kruesi produce a model which he hoped would prove his new theories.

Thomas Alvar Edison 1847-1931

This model consisted of a cylinder supported at each end by a spindle in the form of a screw thread. A handle on the end of the spindle not only made the cylinder revolve, but also it moved along slowly from right to left. The cylinder itself had a spiral groove cut in it with its lines the same distance apart as the screw thread.

Fixed to the base of the machine were two diaphragm and needle units, one for recording, and the other for playing back.

Edison's first phonograph

He wrapped a piece of tinfoil round the cylinder, and while turning the handle shouted into the machine those immortal words beginning "Mary had a little lamb . . .". When he had reached the end of the cylinder he now had a deep line scored in the foil, a line which was pitted with indentations caused by the vibrations of the diaphragm. He cranked the machine back to the beginning, engaged the playback-head and once again turned the handle. Clearly, although somewhat scratchily, his voice came back, "Mary had a little lamb . . .".

His invention fired the imagination of the whole world, and further experiments followed. Wax cylinders replaced tinfoil, and then came records on disc for a machine called the "Graphophone". More inventions and refinements followed as the "talking-machine" became big business. From a musical point of view the severest limitation of these early machines was their limited *frequency response*, that is, they could record only frequencies from about 200 to about 1500 vibrations per second. This of course made the reproduction sound very "boxy", and special orchestral arrangements had to be made, for example, replacing double basses by tubas because the former just wouldn't record as their sound lacked sufficient upper partials. Gramophone horns became larger and larger. Manufacturers even tried coiling them up inside the machine—an invention known as the *expotential horn*.

Nowadays the recording of sound-waves on film, tape, disc and even wire is commonplace, but these are all only extension of the principles discovered in the Phonograph. It is astonishing to realise that our hi-fi stereo recordings of great music are the direct descendants of a scratch on a piece of tinfoil squawking the words "Mary had a little lamb . . .".

APPENDIX V

SIDELIGHTS ON SPEED AND SOUND-WAVE ODDITIES

It is only recently, since aircraft have been breaking the "sound barrier", that the average person has been aware how slowly sound travels. Its speed is nowhere near that of light, being a mere 1,120 feet per second or 750 miles an hour compared with light's 11,000,000 miles a minute or 660,000,000 miles an hour. The light from the sun, which is 93,000,000 miles away, takes under nine minutes to get here; if there were air (at sea-level pressure) between us and the sun, and fortunately there isn't, sound would take about twelve years to cover the same distance.

Incidentally the bang of an aircraft breaking the sound barrier is made by its building up a wave which travels at the same speed as itself, and so causes the "sonic boom".

One recent and amusing discovery is that when a window cleaner flicks his cloth or a Ring-master his whip to make a noise like a pistol shot, its moving tip actually breaks the sound barrier, and he produces a miniature sonic boom. The wave of motion travelling down the cloth or whip has an initial energy-input of, say, an eighth of a horse power for a quarter of a second. This energy becomes concentrated in moving the very tip which weighs virtually nothing. The result is an enormous acceleration to 750 miles an hour or more.

In chapter IX the pressure-waves coming from a sounding body were described as being like peaks and troughs of ripples on a pond. This idea can be extended to the mental picture of low notes producing widely spaced waves, and high notes making ones quite close together. At the same time, the loudness of the sound can be likened to the height of the waves, tiny ripples making quiet notes, and big waves making loud ones. The height of the waves' crests above the troughs would be called the *amplitude* and the distance between two successive waves the *wave length*. A few simple fractions will show that the lowest C on the piano has a wave-length of thirty-five feet while the top C has one of about five inches.

The lowest C vibrates 32 times a second, thus:

$$\frac{1,120}{32} = 35 \text{ feet.}$$

High C vibrates at 2,048 per second, thus:

$$\frac{1,120}{2,048} = .414 \text{ feet}$$

or just under five inches.

A couple of oddities might interest the reader and are worth mentioning.

Doppler Effect

If a fire engine is coming towards you, ringing its bell which sounds, say, C above middle C, the waves would be produced at the rate of 512 per second and the distance between each wave about two feet. The fire engine, on the other hand, is travelling at 40 miles an hour or 60 feet a second, so each vibration from the bell has less far to travel than the previous one to reach our ear. The sound therefore arrives at around 542 vibrations to the second making the sound a tone sharp. Then the engine passes you and starts travelling away, the vibrations you receive become wider apart (the wave-length is increased) and the note drops to about a tone flat—from D down to B♭.

This is known as the *Doppler Effect*, named after Professor Doppler, the physicist who first investigated it.

Resultant Tone

In appendix III mention was made of the "beat" produced by two strings vibrating at slightly different speeds. If one has two very high pitched whistles (even ones producing notes too high to be heard) the beat from the two sounds can itself make a new note called the *resultant tone*. The shrill police-whistle is based on this principle, and is made of two whistles mounted side by side. Readers are recommended to try blowing one while covering one fipplc hole with the fingers so that only one of the two pipes sounds.

Instruments which have very strong upper partials, or overtones,—descant recorders, church bells etc.,—can often produce very strong resultant tones when playing in harmony because the overtones of one note can combine with the overtones of another, and themselves produce such strong resultants that they can mask the main notes being played.

BIBLIOGRAPHY

A book of this size can act only as an introduction to this fascinating subject, and the following books are recommended for further reading.

Historical

Musical Instruments through the Ages. Anthony Baines—Pelican.
Musical Instruments through the Ages. Buchner—Spring Books.
Early Keyboard Instruments. Philip James—Holland Press.

General

Science and Music. Sir James Jeans—Cambridge Press.
The Physics of Music. Alexander Wood—Methuen.
The Instruments of Music. Robert Donnington—Methuen.
Musical Engineering. H. F. Olson—McGraw Hill.
A Textbook of European Musical Instruments. F. W. Galpin—Ernest Benn.

Sound Reproduction

The Fabulous Phonograph. Roland Gelatt—Cassell.
Talking Machines. John Cain—Methuen.
A to Z in Audio. G. A. Briggs—Wharfdale Wireless Works.

INDEX